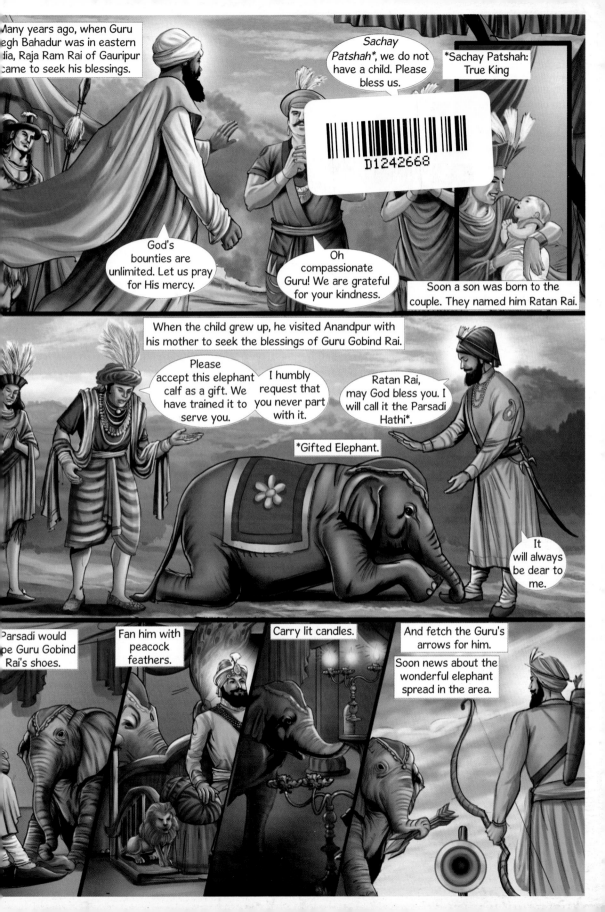

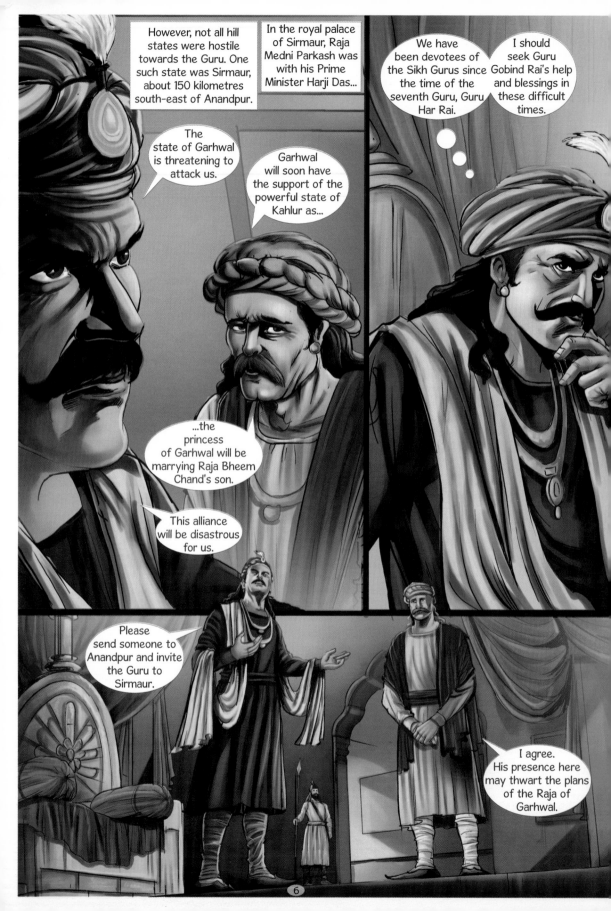

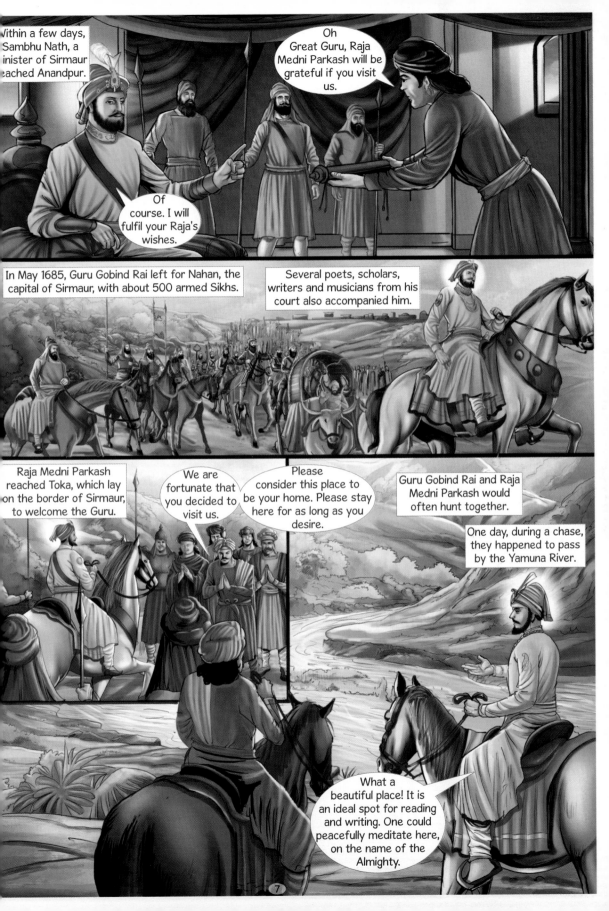

On April 16, 1686, 16 hill Rajas accompanied by several thousand soldiers marched towards Paonta. The 500 Pathans who had betrayed Guru Gobind Rai marched alongside them. They were beating their drums and sounding the battle horns as if they had already won the battle.

Guru Gobind Rai's army only comprised of about 700 men. They were commanded by Daya Ram, Nand Chand, the Guru's uncle Kirpal Chand and the Guru's five cousins, Sango Shah, Jit Mal, Gulab Rai, Sangat Rai and Hari Chand.

Many allies whom we trusted have deserted us.

There is nothing to fear, Akalpurakh is with us.

Continue to chant Waheguru, God's name, and obliterate the enemy.

The valley of Bhangani is six miles from Paonta. We will assemble there...

...and fight the hill Rajas as they cross the Yamuna River.

Guru Gobind Rai ordered Nand Chand and Daya Ram to lead the attack against the Pathans.

The brave heroes let loose a rain of arrows upon the Pathans and sent many to their deaths.

Nand Chand rode into the midst of the enemy, holding a sword in one hand and a lance in the other.

The Guru's cousin Sango Shah and the Pathan chief Najabat Khan succumbed to their injuries after a vicious duel.

He chopped off the heads of many and impaled several others.

Guru Gobind Rai mounted his blue horse and manoeuvred through the battlefield. He led his men forward and targeted the enemy with his arrows.

Many enemy soldiers including the Pathan chief Bhikhan Khan, were killed by the Guru's arrows.

19

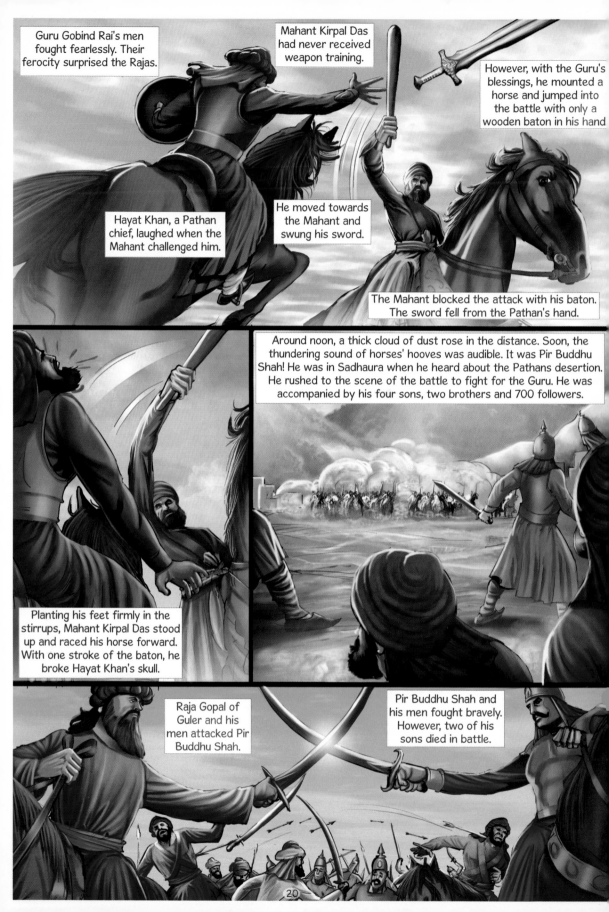

Guru Gobind Rai's men fought fearlessly. Their ferocity surprised the Rajas.

Mahant Kirpal Das had never received weapon training.

However, with the Guru's blessings, he mounted a horse and jumped into the battle with only a wooden baton in his hand

Hayat Khan, a Pathan chief, laughed when the Mahant challenged him.

He moved towards the Mahant and swung his sword.

The Mahant blocked the attack with his baton. The sword fell from the Pathan's hand.

Around noon, a thick cloud of dust rose in the distance. Soon, the thundering sound of horses' hooves was audible. It was Pir Buddhu Shah! He was in Sadhaura when he heard about the Pathans desertion. He rushed to the scene of the battle to fight for the Guru. He was accompanied by his four sons, two brothers and 700 followers.

Planting his feet firmly in the stirrups, Mahant Kirpal Das stood up and raced his horse forward. With one stroke of the baton, he broke Hayat Khan's skull.

Raja Gopal of Guler and his men attacked Pir Buddhu Shah.

Pir Buddhu Shah and his men fought bravely. However, two of his sons died in battle.